Based on the best-selling piano method by Kenneth l

THE COMPLETE PIANO
STANDARDS

Exclusive distributors:
Music Sales Limited
14-15 Berners Street,
London W1T 3LJ, UK.
Music Sales Pty Limited
Units 3-4, 17 Willfox Street, Condell Park
NSW 2200, Australia.

This book © Copyright 2014 by Wise Publications.
Order No. AM1008359
ISBN: 978-1-78305-451-0

Arranged by Derek Jones.
Processed by Paul Ewers Music Design.
Edited by Ruth Power.

Printed in the EU.

Based on the best-selling piano method by Kenneth Baker.

THE COMPLETE PIANO PLAYER
STANDARDS

Wise Publications
London/New York/Paris/Sydney/Copenhagen/Berlin/Madrid/Hong Kong/Tokyo

Always On My Mind

Words & Music by Mark James, Wayne Thompson & Johnny Christopher

mind,
mind,
you were al-ways on my mind.
you were al-ways on my
mind.

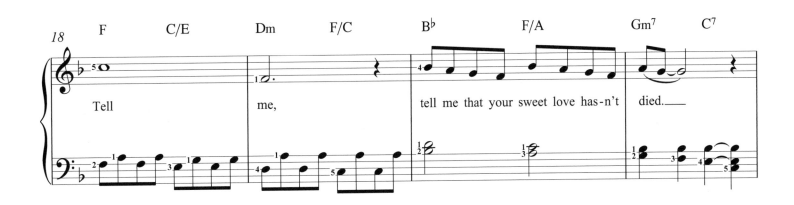

Tell me, tell me that your sweet love has-n't died.____

D.C. al Coda

Give me, give me one more chance to keep you sat - is - fied.____ I'll keep you sat - is -
cresc.
mf

⊕ *Coda*

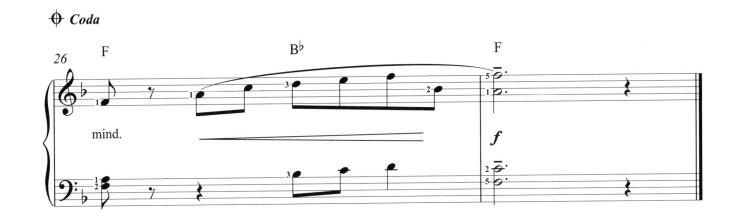

mind.
f

7

At Last

Words by Mack Gordon
Music by Harry Warren

Blue Moon

Words by Lorenz Hart
Music by Richard Rodgers

you heard me say - ing   a prayer for_____   some-one I real - ly could

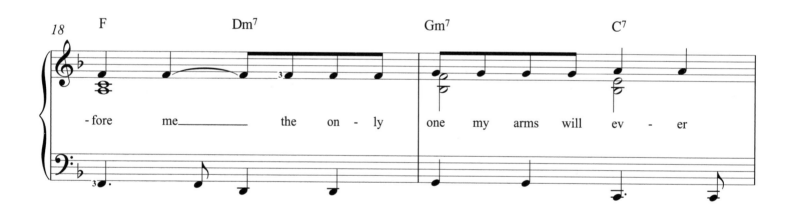

care for.   And then there sud-den-ly____ ap-peared be -

- fore   me_____ the on - ly   one my arms will   ev - er

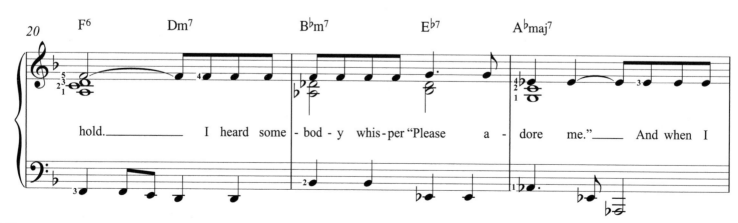

hold._____ I heard some - bod - y whis-per "Please   a - dore me."____ And when I

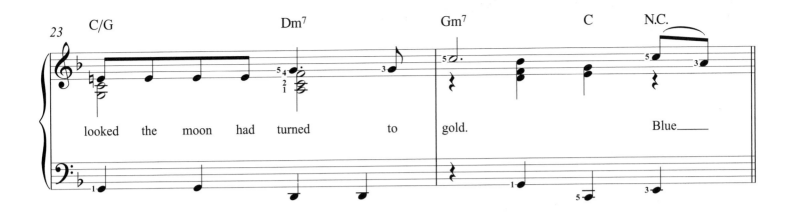

looked the moon had turned to gold. Blue____

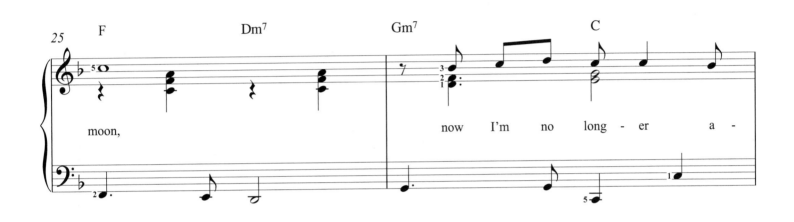

moon, now I'm no long - er a -

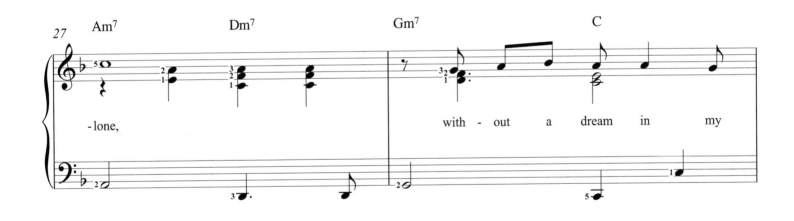

-lone, with - out a dream in my

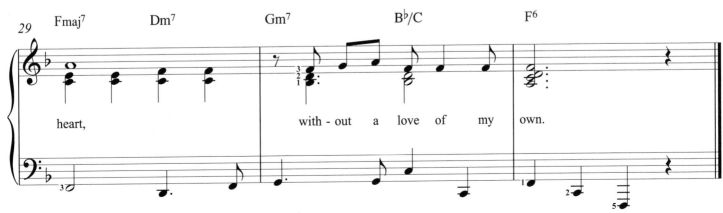

heart, with - out a love of my own.

Bring Me Sunshine

Words by Sylvia Dee
Music by Arthur Kent

Fly Me To The Moon (In Other Words)

Words & Music by Bart Howard

I've Got The World On A String

Words by Ted Koehler
Music by Harold Arlen

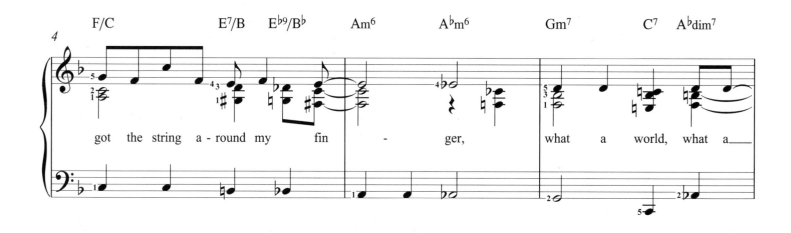

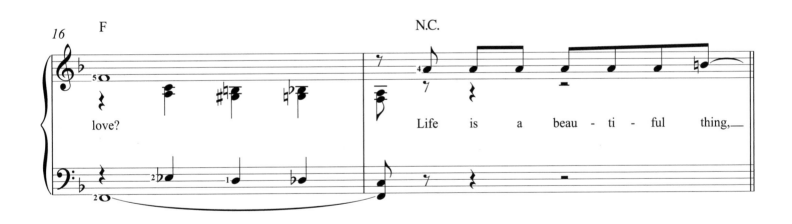

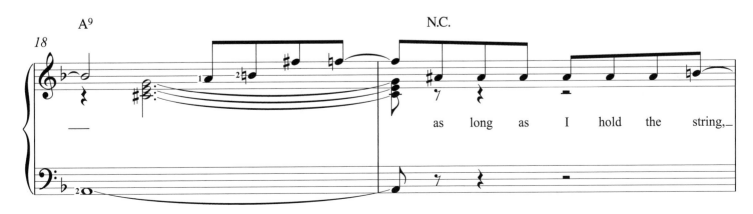

Over The Rainbow (from 'The Wizard Of Oz')

Words by E.Y. Harburg
Music by Harold Arlen

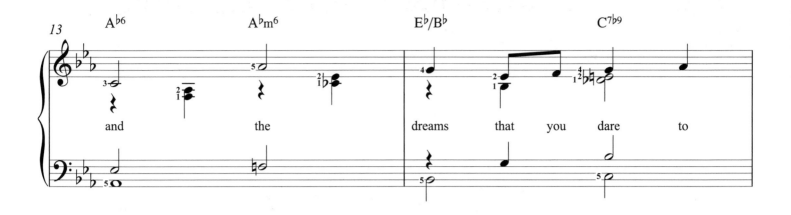

and the dreams that you dare to

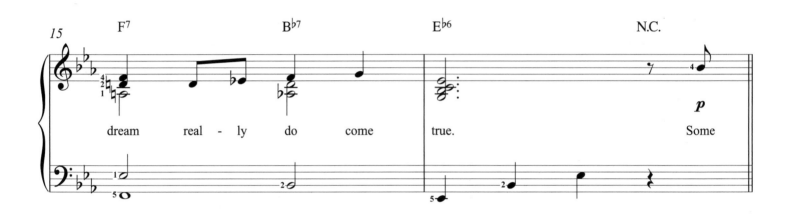

dream real - ly do come true. Some

day I'll wish up-on a star and wake up where the clouds are far be - hind me,

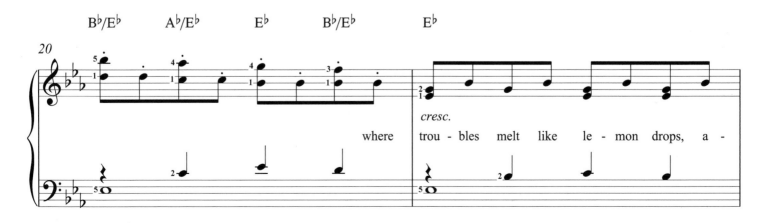

where trou - bles melt like le - mon drops, a -

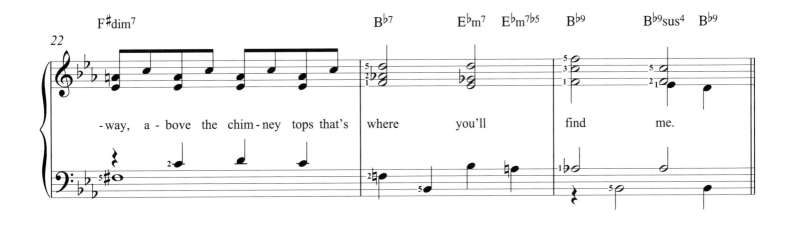

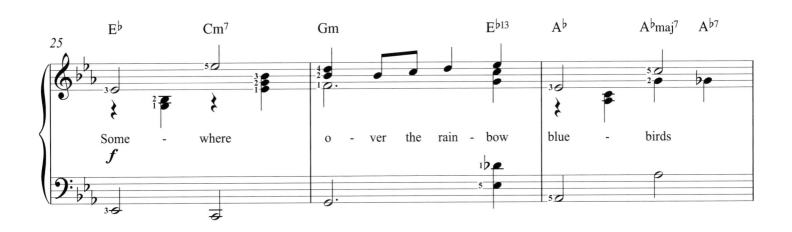

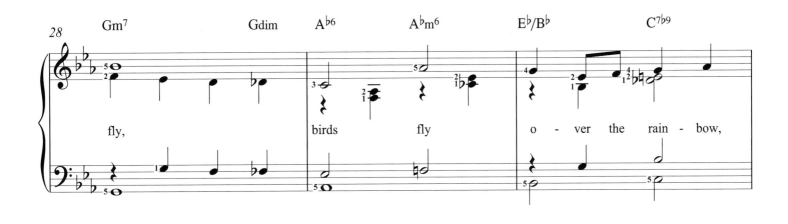

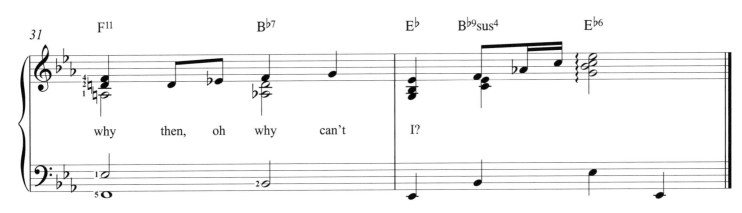

Moon River

Words by Johnny Mercer
Music by Henry Mancini

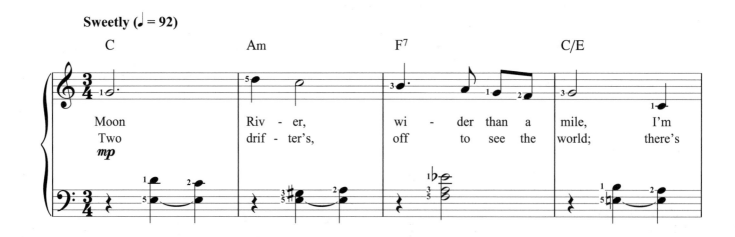

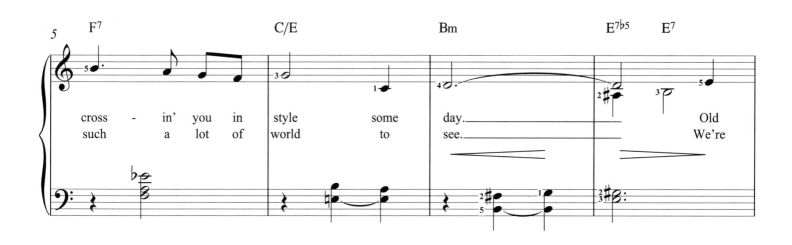

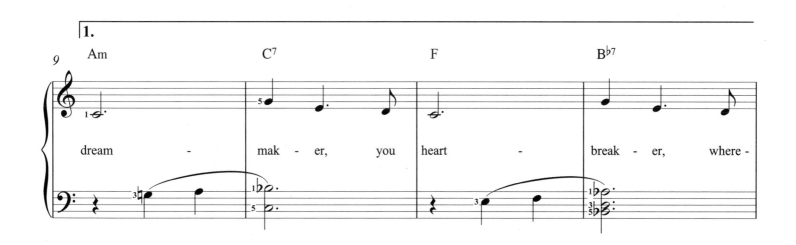

Satin Doll

Words by Johnny Mercer
Music by Duke Ellington & Billy Strayhorn

Take The 'A' Train

Words & Music by Billy Strayhorn

That's Amore

Words & Music by Harry Warren & Jack Brooks

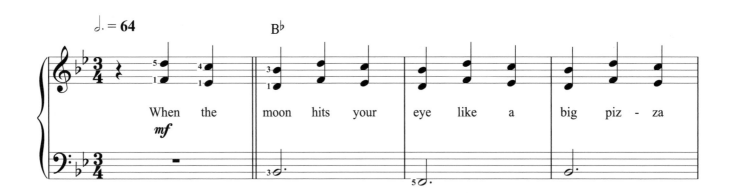

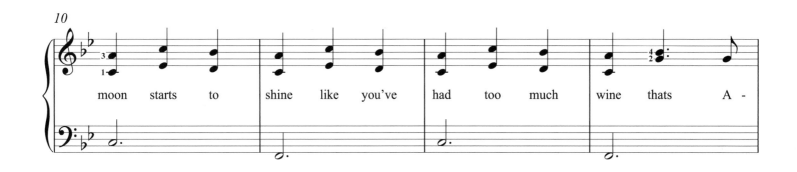

ring ting - a - ling - a - ling,   ting - a - ling - a - ling   and you'll   sing 'Vi - ta

bel - la.'   Hearts   will

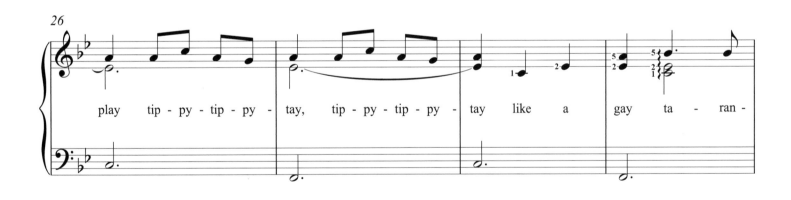

play   tip - py - tip - py - tay,   tip - py - tip - py - tay   like   a   gay   ta - ran -

molto rit.

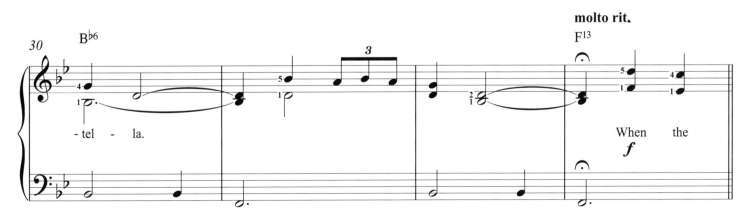

-tel - la.   When   the

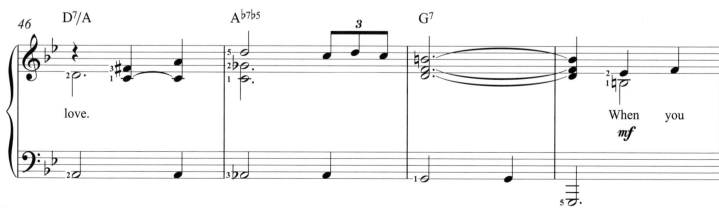

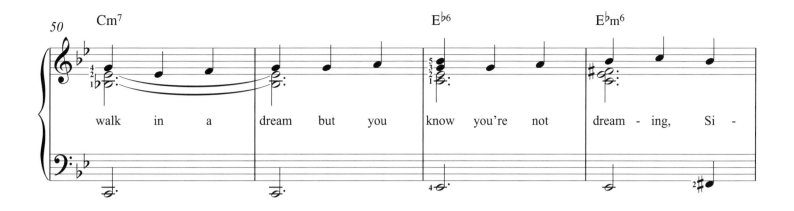

walk in a dream but you know you're not dream - ing, Si -

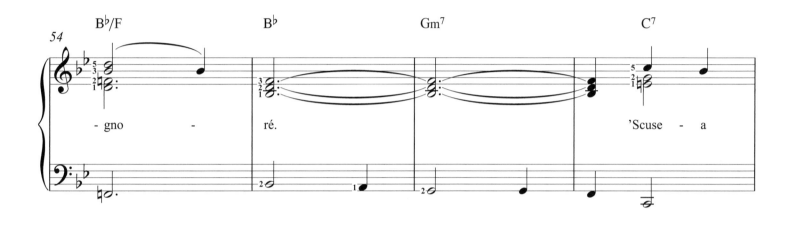

- gno - ré. 'Scuse - a

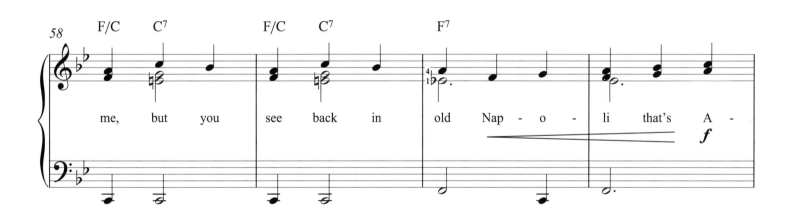

me, but you see back in old Nap - o - li that's A -

- mo - re!

Try A Little Tenderness

Words & Music by Harry Woods, James Campbell & Reginald Connelly

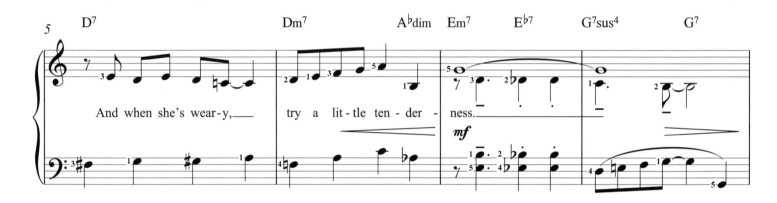

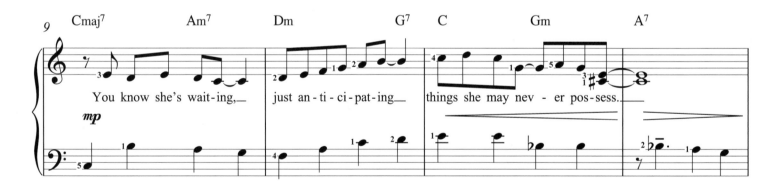

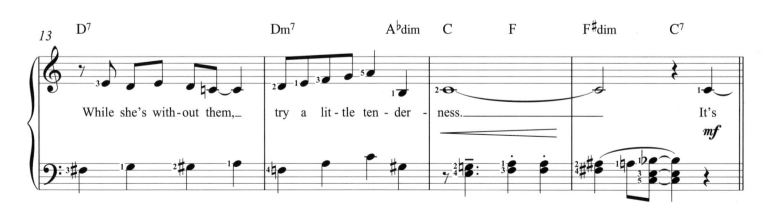

Straight eighths

not just sen - ti - men - tal, she has her grief and care. And a

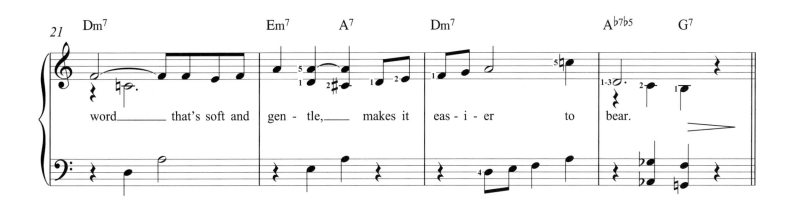

word_____ that's soft and gen - tle,_____ makes it eas - i - er to bear.

With a lilt

You won't re - gret it,___ wo - men don't for - get it,___ love is their whole__ hap - pi - ness.___

mp

(melody)

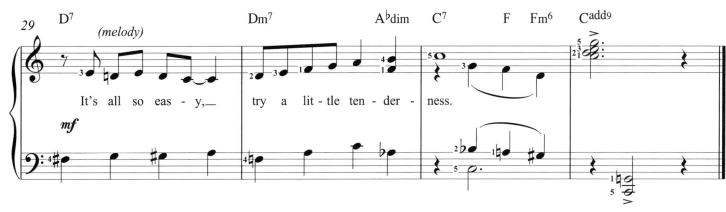

It's all so eas - y,___ try a lit - tle ten - der - ness.

mf

(melody)

The Very Thought Of You

Words & Music by Ray Noble

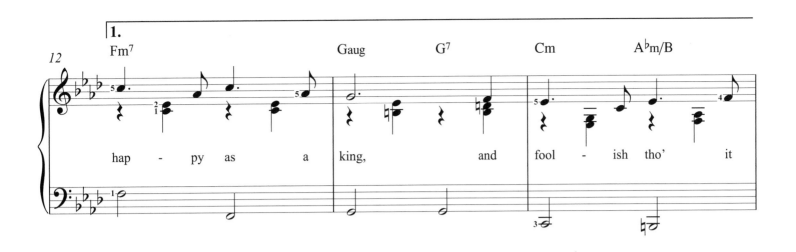

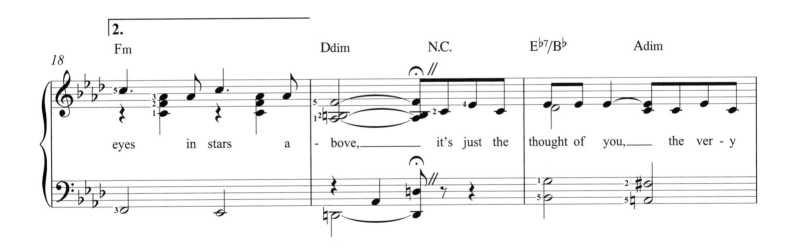

The Way You Look Tonight

Words by Dorothy Fields
Music by Jerome Kern

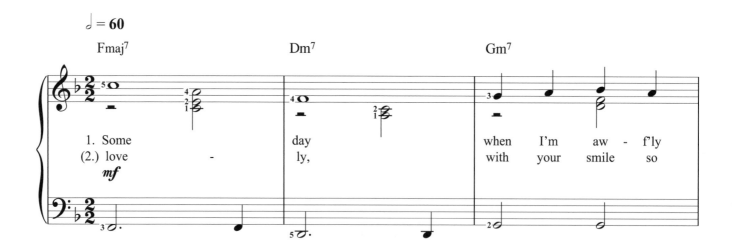

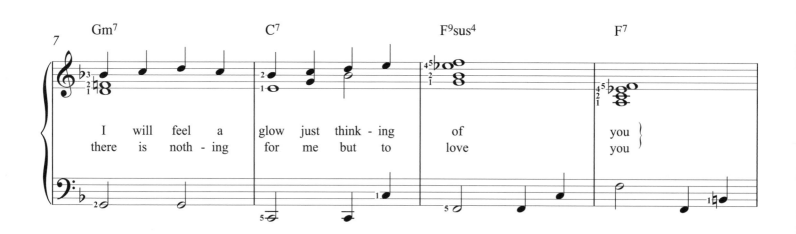

123456789